The Little Church That Grew

The Little Church

LOIS HORTON YOUNG

illustrated by Jim Padgett

THAT GREW

ABINGDON PRESS New York — Nashville

Dedicated to the pastor and
all the wonderful people
of
The Little Church That Grew

Once there was a little church of people who loved God and worked for him, and worshiped together in a little church building.

"Our God is a wonderful God," they said. "We must help our friends and neighbors to know and love him too."

So they invited friends and neighbors to come to the little church. And the friends and neighbors came!

The seats in the little church were full of people. The chairs in the classrooms were full of people.

And when the church services were beginning or ending, the hall was full, full, FULL of people. But still there were many friends and neighbors to be invited.

What a busy place this little church building began to be, with more and more people coming—and always for a reason.

They came to learn how to live in loving-kindness.

They came to grow strong to do right.

They came to talk and to listen, to think about God, to find work to do for him.

They came for weddings, for baptisms, for services of worship.

And nearly all who came said to their friends or neighbors, "Come! Come with us to the little church."

The fathers and mothers held a meeting.

"Our little church building is full of people," they said. "We must build a new church home. There must be room for all who want to come."

"It will take a great deal of money to buy building materials," said one man.

"It will take a great deal of money to pay the workmen," said another.

"But we will give," said a woman. "And if each of us gives what he can, it will be enough."

"And we will work," said another. "This is God's work and he will help us."

The fathers and mothers wrote a letter to the architects. This is what was written in the letter:

"We need a new church home.

We need architects to draw the plans.

Will you make the plans for us?

Will you figure out how much our new church home will cost?"

The architects answered the letter.

"We will draw the plans," they wrote in their letter.

The architects came and looked at the little church building. They looked at the lot on which it was built. They walked around measuring, and measuring, and writing down numbers.

Then the architects
went back to their office.
They began to draw. First
they drew pencil sketches of their ideas.
They filled sheet after sheet of paper
with their sketches until their plans
were the way they wanted them. When
everything was just right, they printed
the drawings on blueprint paper.

These blueprints showed exactly how the new church building would look when it was finished—how it would look inside and outside—and showed exactly how it was to be built.

One blueprint showed where the walls and the doors and the windows would be.

Another showed where the pipes and the plumbing would be.

One blueprint showed where the electric wires, the lights, the switches, and the electric outlets would be. There was a blueprint for the air-conditioning, and

another showed where the furnace would be and how the heat would get through pipes to all the rooms.

The architects made all these blueprints to explain their plans. The architects made a book to tell just how everything in the new church home was to be. It was called the book of specifications.

Then the people of the church held a very important meeting. The architects brought their blueprints and the book of specifications to the meeting.

The people studied the plans. They asked questions. Then they decided.

"We like your plans," they told the architects. "Now we must get a contractor to build the new church home just as the blueprints show him."

So the fathers and the mothers chose a contractor.

They chose the Weaver-Hardin Company. Mr. Hardin talked to the digging men and the stone men and the carpenters. Mr. Weaver talked to the plumbers and the electricians and the painters. Everyone promised to do a good job of building the new church home.

The Weaver-Hardin Company hired Mr. Arnold to be the "boss." It was up to Mr. Arnold to study everything about the architects' plans, and to see that everyone did his work just right, so the new church home would come out strong and beautiful.

Then one day things began to happen.
Along came the bulldozers and the
earth movers and the trucks. Machines
began to dig, to scoop, and shove, and
dump the dirt. They made trenches
where the new walls were to go.

A big, heavy truck came with sand and water and cement all turning around inside until the cement was just right to pour.

The truck's chute was pushed over a trench and out came the cement, slopping and sliding into each trench until it was full of wet, gray cement.

Another truck brought bags of sand and bags of powdery dry cement, hoes, wheelbarrows, and a mixing trough.

Other trucks brought stacks of cement blocks in neat gray rows. And those trucks had cranes that could lift a whole pile of cement blocks at once and put them on the ground without spilling even one!

Cars drove up. Workmen got out of the cars and went to work. These workmen were Richard, Pete, Joe, Sam, Robert, and Harry.

Richard dumped sand and cement into the mixing trough and put in some water from a hose. He took a hoe and mixed the sand and cement and water until it became a sloshy, wet paste called mortar.

Pete and Joe began to lay the cement blocks. They worked carefully to put every block into just the right place.

Sam and Robert and Harry brought mortar in wheelbarrows, and blocks in wheelbarrows, and more mortar and more blocks all day long.

Trucks came with window frames and door frames. And more trucks came with lumber.

Carpenters came with aprons and toolboxes and wooden horses and electric saws. They measured and sawed and hammered, and began to put up the studding and the framing and the forms.

Trucks came with pipes, and trucks came with plumbing and with all the things for the heating.

Plumbers and heating men and air-conditioning men drove up in their cars and began to study the blueprints, so they could put the pipes and the plumbing in just the right places.

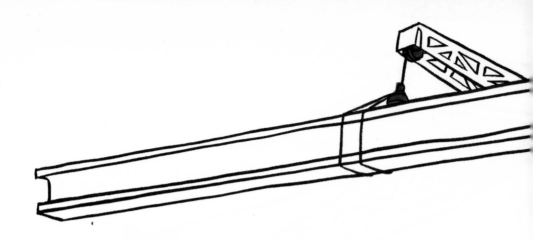

And then there came a tremendous truck with great orange steel girders. Next came a strong cab pulling a tall crane on a low flat trailer. The big crane crawled down slowly, slowly on its caterpillar treads, down from the flat trailer. Slowly the crane's steel cable was swung around to where a man could hook it to a girder. Smoothly the crane turned, swinging the girder to exactly the place where it was needed. And there it stopped for another man to bang the girder into place.

All that day the crane and its operator worked, and the other men worked

to get the pile of girders into a strong steel framework for the new church home.

Now the heavy trucks rumbled back
with cement for the floors. The workmen smoothed the wet cement until the
floors looked like dark gray glass.

Every day Mr. Arnold watched all
the work and checked the blueprints

and the book of specifications to be sure everything was just right.

Every week the contractors, Mr. Weaver and Mr. Hardin, came to see how the work was going.

Every week the architects came to see how their plans were being carried out.

Every Sunday the fathers and the
mothers and the children, and the neighbors and the friends filled the little
church building. After the services
everyone walked around and looked at
the new building, at the walls and the
floors, at the roof and the windows and
the doors.

And people said, "Won't it be wonderful when our new church home is finished? Won't it be wonderful when we

have room enough for everyone who
wants to come here to worship God?
Isn't it exciting to see all the work that
has been done since last Sunday?"

They made pictures with cameras to show how the building changed each week. Boys and girls made crayon pictures to show the building half finished.

The fathers and mothers had a meeting to see what colors the walls were to be and what kinds of tile were to go on

the floor. They decided what kind of organ to put in the building and what kind of furniture to order.

And many people brought their offering envelopes every week with all the money they could give, for everything about a new church home costs money!

All the time the minister worked every day, and most every night, thinking about the church,

praying about the church,
talking with people,
writing letters,
and reading,
visiting people,
and studying,
and planning for the
church.

The electricians came with their coils
of wire and their sockets and their tools.
They put wires in the walls and in
the ceilings, so the new church home

would have lights, and
the organ would work,
the fans would work,
the caretaker could use
the electric cleaner,
the record players would work,
and the projector could show
pictures.

All this time the carpenters were working, putting in windows and making door frames; putting up the studding and putting on the roof; hanging doors, and putting on the trim.

All this time the heating and the air-conditioning men were working with

the pipes, and the valves, and the gauges, and the boiler, and the fuel tanks and the thermostats—working so that when the new church home was finished, all the people could be comfortable.

Workmen came to put glass in the windows.

Ceiling men came to put up the ceiling tile.

Floor men came to put down the floor tile.

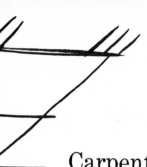

Carpenters put the door knobs, locks, and hinges on the doors and windows.

And pretty soon it was time for the painters! They came with their ladders and their buckets and their brushes and their drop cloths and all their paint in wonderful, wonderful colors.

They painted and painted until everything smelled new and was fresh with color.

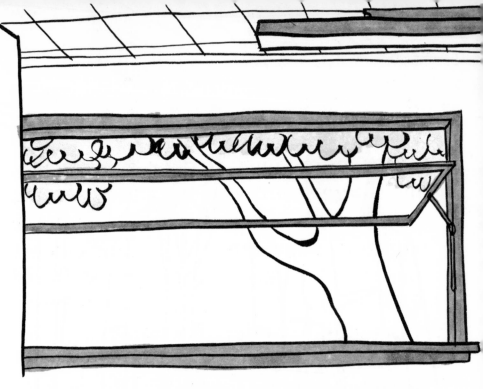

Every Sunday the fathers and the mothers and the children who loved the little church looked at everything the workers had done.

And they said, "It is good. Our new church home will be strong and beautiful. And big enough for all of us to come and worship God. It is good to watch it being built, but it will be even better when it is done!"

A truck brought long boxes of special pipes—pipes of many sizes for the organ. The truck held everything an organ needs, for it had come straight from the organ factory. There were hundreds and hundreds of pieces, and each piece had to go into exactly the right place. Now who would put them there?

Mr. Myers was the organ builder, and he knew just where each piece belonged. When Mr. Myers came to work on the organ, he brought Mr. Miller with him. Together they opened the boxes and took out the pieces, and began to put each one in the right place in the organ chamber. Mr. Myers knew just how to voice the organ and tune it so it would have a beautiful tone for music in praise to God.

Furniture for the new church home
was brought right from the factory
where it was made. Men came on the
truck to unload the pieces of smooth,
shaped wood and stack them into piles.
When the men began to use their drills
and their screws, the pieces of wood

fitted together just right to make
seats.

One Sunday when the people came
they had a big surprise, for the new
church home had seats, an altar, a pul-
pit, a lectern, and a place for the choir.

"Our new church building is almost finished," the people said. "We must plan a dedication."

So the minister and the people planned a special service for the Sunday which was to be the first day for worshiping in the new church home.

They invited all the people who had worked on the building, all the architects and contractors, the stonemasons and electricians, the plumbers and carpenters, the painters and organ builders.

They sent a notice to the newspapers.

They ordered flowers for the altar, and they had a special bulletin printed.

Still there was work to do before everything would be finished.

Men came to lay carpet in the aisles, for the church building would be a quiet place for thinking of God.

Other men fastened the hymn racks, for the people would sing together their praise of God.

And one man brought a table for the guest book, for the church would be a friendly place where visitors would be made welcome.

Everyone was busy, and the minister was busiest of all.

"We must work to have everything ready for Dedication Sunday," the people said.

The organist began to practice on the new organ.

The choirs practiced singing.

The ushers talked about how they would make everyone welcome.

The minister put the big Bible on the new lectern so he could read the Word of God for all to hear.

At last, just in time, everything was ready. The wonderful Sunday was here!

The people began to come. Big people, little people, old people, young people, tall people, short people. Some came walking. Some came riding in cars. The fathers and the mothers and the children came. The friends and the neighbors came. And the men who had built the new building came.

When the organist began to play, almost all the seats were full. When the choirs and the minister came in, all the seats were full!

Then all the people sang a great song of praise to God whom they loved.

Together the people placed on the offering plates their offerings for God, so that their church, which was his church, might be paid for.

Then together the people and the minister stood to join the service of dedication, saying:

"We rejoice that God has put it into the hearts of his people to build this house to the glory of his name.

To God we dedicate this house.

For the worship of God in prayer and
    praise,

For helping families to live rightly,

For leading all of us to do acts of
    kindness,

We dedicate this house.

To the comfort of those who are sad,

To make stronger those who are weak,

To show the way to those who want
    to find it,

We dedicate this house."

Then together all the people made a
promise:
"We now, the people of this church
and this congregation, do promise to
worship and serve our great God
through Jesus Christ our Lord."
And together all the people bowed
their heads, thanking God for this beautiful, strong, good church home where

they could come to think about him.
The minister prayed:

"O God, accept this church home to
be a place where faithful people will
gather to honor thee, the living God;
may this be a house where truth is
spoken for all to hear. Through Jesus
Christ our Lord. Amen."

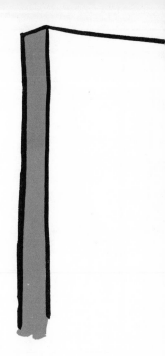

The service of dedication was over, and the people spoke to one another as they went to their homes.

"How lovely is our new church home," they said.

"There is room for all."

"We will work and pray and give."

"We will tell everyone how great is our God."

"The building of our church home is finished, but we will go on working together always to show our love for God."